GIRLS ROCK!

Supporting Learning in Schools

First published in Great Britain by
RISING STARS UK LTD 2008
22 Grafton Street, London W1S 4EX

For information visit our website at:
www.risingstars-uk.com

British Library Cataloguing in Publication Data
A CIP record for this book is available from the British Library.

ISBN: 978 1 84680 269 0

First published in 2008 by
MACMILLAN EDUCATION AUSTRALIA PTY LTD
15–19 Claremont Street, South Yarra 3141

Visit our website at www.macmillan.com.au

Associated companies and representatives throughout the world.

Series created by Felice Arena and Phil Kettle
Project management by Limelight Publishing Services Pty Ltd
Cover and text design by Lore Foye
Illustrations by Meredith Thomas

Printed in China

GiRLS ROCK!
Contents

Mai   Carly

CHAPTER 1

We Wish

Carly and Mai are sitting in the back of Carly's mum's car. They're on the way to the Wimbledon Tennis Championships. Today they'll be watching some of the best tennis players in the world.

Carly "I'd love to play tennis at Wimbledon."

Mai "Yeah, how cool. We could play in the doubles."

Carly "If we did, we'd be the best doubles team in the world."

Mai "Maybe even the best doubles team in the universe."

Carly "I don't think that they play tennis on Mars."

Mai (laughing) "I know. But if they did, we'd be the best there as well."

Carly "I wonder how fast the star players serve the ball?"

Mai "Not sure. But I bet they probably serve it so fast that you might not even be able to see it."

Carly "I wonder if they practise like we do?"

Mai "What? Practise like we do against a brick wall in a park?"

Carly "Well, I think that brick wall practice is the best practice."

Mai "I wonder what it'd be like to play in something as huge as the Wimbledon Championships?"

Carly "Yeah, I wonder? I think it'd be really cool."

Mai "I can't wait to get there."

Carly "Look, here we are now."

CHAPTER 2

What If?

The girls soon get inside the tennis stadium and find their seats at Centre Court.

Mai "You know, after all that training we've done in the park, playing against the brick wall, we should be the ones playing on Centre Court."

Carly "Yeah, how cool would that be? Just look at all the people that are here to watch."

Mai "Well, it's not very often that the fans get to see great players from all over the world."

Carly "Look at all those signs the fans are holding up."

Mai "Yeah. And they all say 'GO FOR IT LEGENDS'. If we were playing, those signs would be for us."

Carly "Yeah. We really are legends, aren't we?"

Mai "Well, we really would be if we could beat the Williams sisters, Venus and Serena."

Carly "Listen! I can hear the announcer."

The announcer tells the crowd that the game has been delayed and that it won't be starting for another hour.

Carly "Hey, listen to the crowds. They're really upset."

Mai "Maybe it's time to go and watch the players practising on the practice courts."

Carly "Do you think that Joel Hoover could be here?"

Mai "Why?"

Carly "No reason. I just wanted to know."

Mai "You really like him don't you?"

Carly "No, no I don't."

Mai "Well, I think he'll be watching the tennis on TV, that's if he's not catching slimy frogs or something else disgusting."

Carly "He's not disgusting!"

Mai "He is too! Last time I saw him he'd been catching frogs. He even tried to put one on my shoulder."

Carly "Yuk! Well if I did like him, I don't now."

Mai "Whatever! Come on, let's hurry up and find the practice courts."

CHAPTER 3

Hi There!

The girls arrange to meet Carly's
mum back at Centre Court in an
hour. They walk around looking at
the different practice courts where
the players are warming up for
their matches.

Mai "Look! It's the Williams sisters."

Carly "We should go and talk to them."

Mai "They won't want to talk to us."

Carly "Well, they might. You don't know."

Mai "But they might not, too."

Mai and Carly work their way through the crowd until they get seats that are really close to the court. They are so close to Venus and Serena, they can almost touch them.

Carly (whispering) "We should ask them for their autographs."

Mai "Yeah. And should we tell them that we practise our tennis against a brick wall?"

Carly "Why should we tell them that?"

Mai "Because if we tell them that, they might think that we're really good players."

Carly "Maybe we should ask them if they'd like to practise against us."

Mai "We'd probably win if we did."

Carly "If we did, I'd serve first."

Mai "How come you'd get to serve first?"

Carly (laughing) "Because I said it
   first."

Mai "So, what would I get to do first?"

Carly "You get to tell the Williams
   sisters that their earrings are way
   too big."

Mai "As if I'm going to tell them that."

Carly "Well, maybe you can tell them
   that we'd thrash them. And that
   we should be playing at Wimbledon
   and not them."

Mai "As if!"

CHAPTER 4

Tongue-tied

Mai and Carly keep watching as
Venus and Serena keep hitting the
ball to each other.

Carly "Wow, they're really good."
Mai "They must hit the ball at three
   hundred kilometres an hour."

Carly "That'd be about the same speed that I hit the ball."

Mai "Well, I think that I could serve the ball even faster than that."

Carly "The Williams sisters would still be able to hit it."

Mai "If I was playing against Venus, I'd serve the ball straight down the centre. It'd be so fast that she'd completely miss it."

Carly "No, she wouldn't. She'd hit it straight back at you."

Mai "Then I'd hit the next one straight at Serena."

Carly "And then she'd hit the ball back at me and I'd smash it right between them both. It'd be a winner."

Mai "Wow! We'd have won a point against the Williams sisters."

Carly "Maybe we should be playing at Wimbledon after all."

Just then, Venus hits the ball to Serena, who misses it. The ball lands at the feet of Mai and Carly.

Carly (picking up the ball) "Do you think they're going to come and get it?"

Mai "Maybe you should throw it back to them."

Venus starts walking towards the girls.

Carly "Hey! Look! Here comes Venus."

Mai "Wow! And here comes Serena as well."

Carly "So what are we going to say
  to them?"
Mai "Quick! Think of something
  interesting."

Before Mai and Carly can think of
anything to say, Venus and Serena
are standing in front of them. Mai
and Carly are tongue-tied.

CHAPTER 5

Winners Are Grinners

After chatting for a couple of minutes, Venus and Serena take their ball from Mai and Carly and then go back to practising.

Carly "Well, you really mucked that up."

Mai "What do you mean, *I* mucked it up? All I did was tell her what big earrings she had."

Carly "Yeah, well, lucky I told her they looked really good."

Mai "That's true, but then *you* were the one who told them how much we loved tennis, that we practised against a brick wall in the park."

Carly "Yeah, well, I couldn't think of anything else to say."

Mai "Still, you didn't have to tell them that maybe we'd be good enough to beat them in a couple of years."

Carly "Yeah, well, I reckon that if we practise as hard as they do, we might be as good as them one day."

Mai "Look! They're finished, and
   they're coming over here again."
Carly "Don't you say anything."
Mai "Why me?"

The Williams sisters come back to
where the girls are sitting and ask
them if they'd like to have a tennis
racket each, and a signed tennis ball.
Carly and Mai are thrilled.

Carly "Let's go and find Mum. She's never going to believe us!"

Mai "That was so cool. I can't believe we not only met the Williams sisters, but they gave us these great rackets and balls as well."

Carly "Me neither. It's so exciting. They must've thought we were their best fans."

Mai "I can't wait to tell everyone the story and to show off my new tennis racket."

Carly "Neither can I."

Mai "I'm going to put my signed ball in a special box at home."

Carly "Me too."

Mai "All of our friends will be so jealous."

As they return to Centre Court, the players have just come out and the main match is about to start. The girls meet Carly's mother and tell her what happened. They show her their new rackets and balls.

Mai "How long do you think it'll be before we're good enough to play at the Wimbledon Championships?"

Carly "A long time yet. Depends how much practice we can do. Probably next year."

Mai "Now I can't wait to get home."

Carly "Why? We can't go now. We've
got the real match to watch on
Centre Court."

Mai "Yeah, I know, but I also want to
get home so I can practise against
the brick wall."

Carly "Yeah, with our new rackets."

GIRLS ROCK!
Tennis Lingo

Mai

Carly

ace A ball that you serve that the player on the other side cannot hit back because it's going so fast.

doubles When two players play together on the same team, they are playing doubles.

legends This is what Mai and Carly think they are. Legends are people that everyone else knows about, because they are so good.

lob A really high ball that goes over to the back of the players that you are playing against.

net A net runs across the middle of the court. You have to hit the ball over the net.

GIRLS ROCK!
Tennis Must-dos

☆ Learn to play really good backhand shots as well as forehand shots.

☆ Never argue with the umpire. The umpire's decision is always final.

☆ If you are going to do a lob shot, just make sure that there are no low-flying planes or birds overhead.

☆ If you are practising against a brick wall, always remember that the harder you hit the ball, the harder it comes back at you.

☆ If you want to be as good as the Williams sisters, then you have to practise a lot—and it doesn't really matter if you wear earrings or not.

☆ If you like to wear really big earrings, make sure that they're not heavy or they'll stretch your earlobes.

☆ If you're playing doubles against a team that is as good as Mai and Carly, make sure that you wear a helmet. You never know when you might get hit in the head by a flying tennis ball—and that would really hurt!

☆ Remember if you go to the Wimbledon Championships, the matches are shown on national TV, so make sure you behave!

Tennis Instant Info

Tennis is played in most countries in the world.

Two people can play tennis with one player on each side of the net. This is called singles. Four people can also play tennis with two players on each side of the net. This is called doubles.

Tennis is played on different surfaces. You can play on clay, grass or a special surface called rebound ace.

Ball boys and ball girls are the people who collect the balls in between points, and give the players new balls.

A deuce is when the scores in a tennis game are even at three points each.

The major tennis tournaments each year are: the French Open, the US Open, the Australian Open and the Wimbledon tournament in England.

If a singles tennis player or a doubles team wins all four of these tournaments in the same year, they have won the Grand Slam.

When you are saying the score in a tennis match, the word "love" means zero.

Think Tank

1   How many players are there on the tennis court in a game of doubles?

2   Are girls better tennis players than boys?

3   If you have been aced, what has happened?

4   If you hit a lob shot, does the ball go high in the air?

5   Who are the best female doubles team in the world?

6   If the umpire calls "deuce" what is happening?

7   Does wearing sunglasses make you play better?

8   If you are a left-handed player and you hit a backhand shot, what side of your body have you hit the ball on?

Answers

1 There are four players on the court in a game of doubles.

2 Yes! Of course girls are better tennis players than boys.

3 If you have been aced, you have missed a ball that has been served to you.

4 Yes. When you hit a lob, the ball goes high in the air.

5 Mai and Carly are the best doubles team in the world.

6 If the umpire calls ''deuce'', the score in a game is three points for each player.

7 No. Wearing sunglasses doesn't make you play better, but it might make you look better.

8 If you are left-handed, you will hit a backhand shot on the right side of your body.

How did you score?

- If you got all 8 answers correct, then you're probably good enough to play Mai and Carly.

- If you got 6 answers correct, then you might only be good enough to play the Williams sisters.

- If you got fewer than 4 answers correct, then maybe you should think about playing football instead.

Hey Girls!

I hope that you had as much fun reading my story as I had writing it. I loved reading and writing stories when I was young. And in the stories that I wrote, I was always better than I actually was in real life. It was great fun!

At school, why don't you use "Doubles Trouble" as a play and you and your friends can be the actors. You can dress up in your tennis gear. Don't forget to bring your tennis racquet, and if the school has a stage you can pretend that it is a tennis court.

So ... have you decided who's going to be Mai and who's going to be Carly? And who's going to serve? Make sure that you only pretend to serve the ball or else you might get into trouble.

Make sure that you take this story home and get someone to read it out loud to you, or even act out the parts with you.

Reading at home is lots of fun and really important!

And remember, Girls Rock!

Sheyfettle.

GIRLS ROCK!
When We Were Kids

Shey

Holly

Shey talked to Holly, another *Girls Rock!* author.

Holly "Were you good at tennis when you were young?"

Shey "Yep! I was great."

Holly "So what made you great at tennis?"

Shey "I played against my older brothers all the time so I had to try really hard."

Holly "So, did you ever beat them?"

Shey "Oh yes. Not only did I beat *them*, I beat another boy who was really good."

Holly "So what did the boy do?"

Shey "He cried."

Holly "So Girls Rock at tennis?"

Shey "They do!"

GIRLS ROCK!
What a Laugh!

Q Why was Cinderella hopeless at tennis?

A Because she had a pumpkin as a coach!

GIRLS ROCK!

Read about the fun that girls have in these *GIRLS ROCK!* titles:

Birthday Party Blues
Pony Club

Doubles Trouble
Football Crazy

Dance Fever
Minigolf Face-off

Trapeze Dreams
Two at the Zoo

... and 20 more great titles to choose from!

GIRLS ROCK! books are available from most booksellers. For mail order information please call Rising Stars on 0871 47 23 010 or visit www.risingstars-uk.com

44